The Forward & Backward City

Published and distributed by:
Voices of Future Generations International Children's Book Series
Trust for Sustainable Living
Hampstead Norreys, Berkshire, RG18 0TN, United Kingdom
Tel: +44 (0)1635 202444
Web: www.vofg.org

Special thanks to René V. Steiner for layout and graphics support:
www.steinergraphics.com.

The Voices of Future Generations International Children's Book Series:
'The Epic Eco-Inventions' by Jona David (Europe/North America), illustrated by Carol Adlam
'The Great Green Vine Invention' by Jona David (Europe/North America), illustrated by Carol Adlam
'The Tree of Hope' by Kehkashan Basu (Middle East), illustrated by Karen Webb-Meek
'The Fireflies After the Typhoon' by Anna Kuo (Asia), illustrated by Siri Vinter
'The Species-Saving Time Team' by Lautaro Real (Latin America), illustrated by Dan Ungureanu
'The Sisters' Mind Connection' by Allison Lievano-Gomez (Latin America), illustrated by Oscar Pinto
'The Forward and Backward City' by Diwa Boateng (Africa), illustrated by Meryl Treatner
'The Voice of an Island' by Lupe Vaai (Pacific Islands), illustrated by Li-Wen Chu
'The Visible Girls' by Tyronah Sioni (Pacific Islands), illustrated by Kasia Nieżywińska
'The Mechanical Chess Invention' by Jona David (Europe/North America), illustrated by Dan Ungureanu

Under the patronage of
UNESCO

United Nations
Educational, Scientific and
Cultural Organization

This book is printed on recycled paper, using sustainable and low-carbon printing methods.

The
Forward & Backward
City

by

Diwa Boateng

Illustrated by Meryl Treater

foreword

A love of reading books is one of life's greatest blessings. For not only is reading key to thinking, learning and finding answers to the challenges we face, but it is also a comfort and joy. And so the publication of a series of books by children for children is a wonderful way to mark the 25th anniversary of the adoption of the United Nations Convention on the Rights of the Child. Young Diwa Boateng's book *The Forward and Backward City,* although set in a fictional city, tells a story that is all too real in our contemporary world. It is about two children of the same age growing up in the same city in starkly different social and economic circumstances. It reminds us of the important promises that are contained in the Convention on the Rights of the Child and the road we still have to travel to deliver on those promises. Achieving a world in which the rights of all children are protected and fulfilled is a task for this and future generations. Diwa Boateng's story reminds all his readers that we cannot shirk this task. Thank you, Diwa! And congratulations too to the United Nations Voices of Future Generations Initiative on Children's Rights and Sustainable Development on the publication of this series of books.

Kate O'Regan
Former Judge of the Constitutional Court of South Africa
Director, Bonavero Institute of Human Rights, University of Oxford

foreword

In the same year that world leaders adopt the Post-2015 Sustainable Development Goals, this book is proof that the brave and bright ideas of boys and girls can improve the lives of their communities and deliver a better and more sustainable future to their children's children.

Child Author Diwa Boateng has shown that, backed by a sense of adventure and sheer bravery, children can expose the scandals that lead to the deprivation of basic rights that are crucial to equitable sustainable development. He shows how the inherent power of friendship can shatter the barriers caused by corruption and inequality and transform children into leaders of society that help the world achieve a more sustainable future.

The Voices of Future Generations Children's Book Series, which educates children about their fundamental rights and the role they can play in sustainable development, not only makes an important contribution to the world's collective goal of attaining sustainable development but helps shape children's ideas about the future they want. It is a personal pleasure to commend this marvellous children's book to you, our upcoming generations of readers, writers and leaders.

Mr Nikhil Seth
Former Director, United Nations Division on Sustainable Development

preface

The Voices of Future Generations Children's Book Series is an effective means through which children can lead the process of creating the future they want to live in. It also places adults under an important responsibility to deliver a better destiny for the generations of today and tomorrow.

The Forward and Backward City is an important reminder that the spirit of fearless courage, determination and unity dwells in children, even in the face of inequality, lack of resources, poverty and other pressures. This book warns the world and its leaders that corruption depletes much needed resources that can prevent children from accessing food, clean water, healthcare, education and a dignified standard of living. It contains an imaginative, yet powerful message telling the world that by enriching a few, corruption leaves many innocent children to live a life of poverty and indignity and robs them of their fundamental rights. Through this book, Diwa Boateng has succeeded in showing us that corruption has no place in the world today and future generations do not deserve to experience its effects. Indeed, *The Forward and Backward City* reminds us all that if the world's agenda on sustainable development is to be achieved successfully, then children's rights have to be respected, upheld and accessed.

The issues raised in the stories in the Voices of Future Generations Children's Book Series contain important lessons on how children want their rights to be respected and should be read by all those working towards a brighter future.

Dr. Ashfaq Khalfan
Director, Law and Policy Programme,
Amnesty International

chapter 1

It is 2030 and Kabwe is playing with his handheld Infin8r machine at school. He heard from his father that in the year 2000, schools used to have blackboards and actual teachers with text books and chalk boards.

Kabwe tries to imagine how this could have been but he can't – all he knows is that it must have been soooo boring. He is just thankful that he has a virtual library, a virtual teacher, a virtual pen and paper and school is such fun.

Kabwe lives with his mother and father in the Savannah Grasslands of Africa, in the beautiful city of Madini. Madini is a bright city built on top of many precious minerals. The Tibela River divides the city into Madini North and Madini South. Kabwe lives in Madini North. It is ultra modern. It is built using the latest advanced technology.

Kabwe's father is the Mayor of Madini. They live in a castle on the top of a hill in the centre of the city. The castle roof is made of gold, with door-knobs of polished diamonds. The family eats from emerald plates with platinum forks and knives. They drink from rhodium goblets.

Their baths are made of titanium and they bathe in mineral rich spring water. Their food, including vegetables, is all genetically enhanced to make it more juicy, nutritious and healthy. They have many servants and many gadgets which do everything for them.

There is only one problem: Kabwe is an only child and he is very lonely. He has grown tired of his Infin8r and longs to have someone real to play with. He also loves to read but he only has a few collector's item paperback and hardback children's story books. He can only read them on the weekend when he is resting from all his technology.

He stacks them on his bedroom windowsill which is always open because the gadgets and minerals make the house very hot. Kabwe has a secret wish – he keeps his window open all day and night because he prays that an imaginary friend could come and find him one day.

chapter 2

All the servants working in the castle come from the other part of the city, Madini South, where life is tough. There is no pure water and big families cram themselves into small houses.

They only share some porridge and fish from the river, once a day. Parents leave home early in the morning to work. Some work in houses and castles like Kabwe's. Others go fishing and sell fish, iced water, groundnuts and other wares on the roadside. There are no more schools in this part of the city because the money for classrooms and books is spent in Madini North, Kabwe's part of the city. But, there is lots of room to play in the dust, even until sundown.

The children in this part of the city have many friends and they create their own games and toys, like cars and aeroplanes made of wire, cans and plastic bottles. They invent stick-fighting martial arts games and board games using cardboard and smooth stones.

They have turned the inside and outside walls of their houses into picture murals of the future they want to see. This future has schools, teachers and books, roads, clean water, hospitals and lots of food. They also imagine having toys and educational gadgets to play with. Above all, they wish they could also live in big houses like the people in Madini North.

chapter 3

One of the servants in Kabwe's house is a happy woman called Shamiso. She is a struggling widow with six children. She leaves them early every morning to go to work at Kabwe's house. She loves him like her own son and does everything for him like cooking, cleaning, bathing and other things he can actually do by himself.

Everyday she tells him about her son Tatenda who is also 9 years old and was born on the same day as Kabwe. She shares stories about the creative toys Tatenda makes to play with. When she goes home every night, she tells Tatenda and her other children about Kabwe and all his gadgets.

Every night at bedtime, the powerful technological light beams from Kabwe's castle on the hill bounce off the Tibela River and shine into Tatenda's dark home. One Saturday night, Tatenda has to go to bed hungry and he cannot sleep. He is missing his best friend Sahwira (pronounced Sa-h-weera). Sadly, there has been an epidemic sweeping the land. Sahwira had to leave the city and return to his village with his family to take care of his aunties and uncles and cousins who live there. Tatenda is worried because he does not know if and when his best friend will come back to the city.

He also cannot hold his curiosity about Kabwe any longer so he decides to sail his father's rickety kayak to Kabwe's home. He climbs the hill and finds Kabwe's bedroom window open with the stack of books on the windowsill.

He overhears the mayor and his wife yawning as they tell Kabwe that they are going to bed and he should finish playing with his Infin8r soon and sleep too.

chapter 4

Tatenda takes a deep breath and sneaks into the bedroom through the open window. He borrows a very interesting looking book in the pile of Kabwe's books and puts it in his rucksack. He makes his way to the kitchen, hoping to rummage for food. He opens what looks like a fridge and he can't believe all the kinds of delicious food he finds!

As Tatenda is about to bite into a piece of juicy chicken, he suddenly hears footsteps coming towards him. He starts to panic and sweat fills his brow and prickles his armpits. It is too late to run and he freezes when a boy who fits Shamiso's description of Kabwe points a flashlight at him and threatens to set off the alarm with the remote in his hand. It is Kabwe and although he is also scared, he boldly asks Tatenda "Who are you?!"

"Please. It's Ta-ta-tenda …I am Sh-Shamiso's son. I live in the other part of the city. I am very hungry. Please forgive me. Sorry…" Tatenda replies as he drops the piece of chicken. The boys stare at each other nervously and are unsure of what to do or say next. They stand and stare at each other with hearts beating loudly in the awkward silence.

To Kabwe, Tatenda looks thinner but taller than he had imagined from Shamiso's stories. Kabwe thinks Tatenda's clothes look like a ragged and dirty uniform and his hair looks very coiled and hard, like it has never been combed. Tatenda also smells a bit sweaty but Kabwe has figured out that this must be because of fear and the heat in the house.

To Tatenda, Kabwe seems rounder, shorter and more plump than Tatenda had imagined from Shamiso's stories. He is dressed like a prince in the finest African silk and linen pyjamas with fine, soft leather sandals.

Just as Tatenda is trying to think of what to say, the book falls out of the rucksack. Kabwe's face lights up because he thinks the book, which he loves, belongs to Tatenda and that they must have something in common! They both bend down to pick the book and bump their heads. They smile nervously into each others' eyes and their smiles warmly soften the tense atmosphere. Kabwe breaks the silence by asking how Tatenda got into the house and they end up spending hours getting to know each other. Tatenda confesses to having borrowed Kabwe's book and the next thing they know, they are best friends.

Kabwe offers Tatenda some sweet water to drink and fills the table with a lot of food. Kabwe eats until he is too full. They then spend several hours looking at all Kabwe's toys and gadgets. Tatenda's other friend Langa had a gadget but it was made in 2012 and it has broken down from over use by many of children because Langa generously lent it to everyone. When Kabwe demonstrates how the cyber world of the Infin8r works, tears well up in Tatenda's eyes. He tries to hide them, but a big one falls on to the screen of the Infin8r.

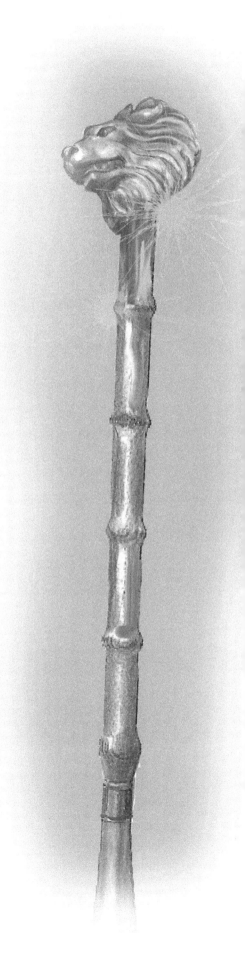

He explains to Kabwe that where he comes from, children do not get these kinds of gadgets and toys. Kabwe is shocked and devastated to hear that they do not even have schools! He cannot believe that there are no school resources in Madini South when he and his classmates have left old versions of their Infin8rs lying around. These wasted gadgets are still perfectly useful but are now gathering dust in basements and sheds all over Madini North.

Speaking of his home reminds Tatenda that it is time for him to go back. Kabwe fills Tatenda's rucksack with bottles of sweet water, lots of chicken, fruits and delicious vegetables to take home. Tatenda leaves feeling happy that his family will be glad to be eating something other than fish for the next few days.

chapter 5

Kabwe goes to bed knowing that he will have to talk to his father about building schools in Tatenda's part of the city. When his parents wake up, he tells them about Tatenda and what he said. His father is worried about how Tatenda made it into the house but he is more shocked about the plight of the children in Madini South. He is angry because the Deputy Mayor and his team have always been in charge of Tatenda's area.

The mayor checks his Infin8rXX for information and finds statements from the Deputy Mayor showing the number of schools, hospitals, water treatment plants and houses which were supposedly built in Madini South in the last five years. Kabwe says he believes Tatenda and that nothing was actually done at all. Kabwe's father believes his son.

That week, the Mayor carries out what he calls a special "Forensic Financial Investigation" on what the Deputy Mayor has been doing. He finds that the Deputy Mayor and his team have been keeping all the money that was meant for Tatenda and the other families, for themselves. They have used it to buy the latest fleet of highly technologically advanced and customised Cheetah cars which move at 300km an hour and hidden them in secret garages. They have equipped their houses with robots which do everything for them.

Shockingly, the Deputy Mayor's wife is bathing in milk and using gold dust as make-up! The Deputy Mayor has also filled a special bunker with vaults of cash. It seems the list of so many selfish and unfair things done with the money is endless. The Mayor is very angry and sad because this has left Tatenda and other people to suffer.

After the investigation is completed, the Mayor decides to hold a ceremony to honour Tatenda's bravery in exposing the problems in his city. The Mayor's speech at the ceremony mentions something called the UN Convention on the Rights of the Child, from many years ago, which says all children should have an education, clean water, a clean environment, a right to play, a right to be heard and lots of other nice things.

Tatenda cannot believe his ears that there is such a global promise and he cannot wait to find out about it. Just as Tatenda is daydreaming about the Convention, he is asked to come to the podium. To his compete surprise the Mayor says that Tatenda is being appointed as a Junior Mayor for his part of the city! Before he can figure out what this means, there is a large roar of applause and he is being draped in a heavy gold chain with lots of medallions which look like large coins.

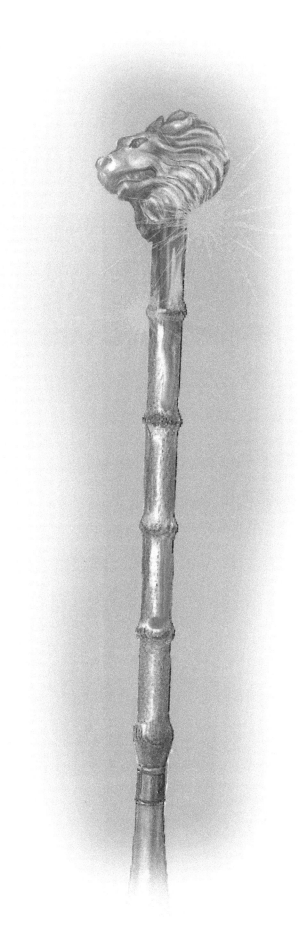

He is also handed a custom made rhodium walking stick with the symbol of Madini, a large lion's face. The mayor calls it the Mayoral Mace. While Tatenda is admiring the lions head, he is also handed a thick golden envelope with a golden seal of the face of a lion. As Tatenda stands there in the midst of the applause, he knows that this all means his life will never be the same.

After the ceremony, Tatenda and his family are invited to the Mayor's castle on the hill for a feast. The Mayor, his wife and Kabwe are dressed as waiters and they serve Tatenda's family. Everyone thinks this is funny but they, especially Shamiso, feel very important for the first time.

To crown the day, the Mayor makes sure that Tatenda and his family are taken home in the Mayor's official yacht. Even Tatenda's older brothers are being extra nice to him that night. Tatenda can't believe all the things that have happened today. It is the best day of his life and he only wishes that Sahwira could have been there beside him.

Just before bed, he remembers to open the envelope. It is written on official paper which is embossed with the Madini Lion. This is what the letter says:

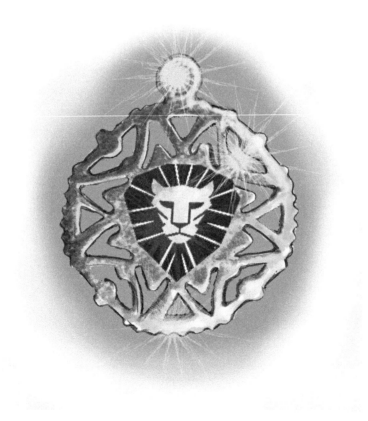

Dear Tatenda Gamba,

The City of Madini would like to congratulate you for uncovering corruption. In recognition of your efforts, the City of Madini is pleased to appoint you as Junior Mayor of the area South of Madini. This means you will be responsible for investigating whether the children in Madini South are enjoying the rights they have been guaranteed in the UN Convention on the Rights of the Child. The Convention is enclosed with this letter. Please read and understand it as it will be your investigative guide. Please find a team of girls and boys to help you in your investigations. You will report all your findings to me, the Mayor of Madini during a special meeting at my offices every month. I look forward to working with you.

Well done and congratulations!

Yours Faithfully
The Mayor of Madini
Signed on this 15th day of February 2030 in the City of Madini.

It is bed time but Tatenda is joyful, excited and shocked. He can't believe this is really him. He has trouble sleeping because so many thoughts are competing for his attention. He is thinking about who he can invite to join his team, what investigations they will carry out, how they will work, whether they should have uniforms and so many other things. He really wishes that instead of being out fighting the terrible epidemic in the countryside, Shamwari would come back soon and help him. Just then, he remembers that he will have to study this Convention document which is in the letter. It looks long, with many articles, and very important but he knows that since he loves reading, he will study it very hard.

Before he falls asleep, he imagines the new future he will have now that this so-called corruption scheme has been uncovered. Although he is lying on a small bed with two of his brothers, he imagines that, in the future, he will live in a home with adequate space and that all families in Madini South will have healthy food and water and hopefully medicine to fight epidemics. He breathes a sigh of relief and drifts off into a deep, restful sleep, dreaming about his bright future.

The End.

about the author

Diwa Boateng was born in Cape Town in 2005 to a West African father and a Southern African mother. He carried out research for his story in South Africa, Ghana, Zambia and Zimbabwe and is very passionate about the right of every child in Africa to equal opportunities to advance in life through education.

In 2015, Diwa was appointed United Nations Child Ambassador for the post-2015 Sustainable Development Goals. He is also a skilled computer game programmer who enjoys creating artwork and animations.

Diwa is an avid reader and his book is dedicated to his late grandfathers, his grandmother who lives in South Africa and his other grandmother who lives in Ghana. Diwa also dedicates this book to his parents and all the children in Africa who inspired him to write it.

about the illustrator

Meryl Treatner holds degrees from the University of the Arts in Philadelphia, USA Meryl's illustrations have appeared in hundreds of leading newspapers and magazines. Her cover art depicting child abuse won a Best Magazine Cover award judged and exhibited by Art Direction Magazine and appeared in their Creativity Annual. Her artwork has also been exhibited in the Lowe Gallery, Syracuse University, and the Huntsville, Alabama Museum of Art.

Meryl is also an experienced courtroom sketch artist and her courtroom sketches have been featured by ABC Nightly News and United Press International.

The publishers for which Meryl has illustrated include Pearson Learning Group, Random House, Scott-Foresman, McGraw-Hill School Division, Hampton-Brown, Harcourt-Brace-Jovanovich, Wm. Morrow and Company, Scholastic Books, National Geographic Books, Dell Yearling, Saxon Publishers, Rigby, Richard C. Owen Publishers and Creative Teaching Press.

Meryl lives with her husband and three children in Philadelphia, USA.

The United Nations Convention on the Rights of the Child

All children are holders of important human rights. Twenty-five years ago in 1989, over a hundred countries agreed a UN Convention on the Rights of the Child. In the most important human rights treaty in history, they promised to protect and promote all children's equal rights, which are connected and equally important.

In the 54 Articles of the Convention, countries make solemn promises to defend children's needs and dreams. They recognize the role of children in realizing their rights, being heard and involved in decisions. Especially, Article 24 and Article 27 defend children's rights to safe drinking water, good food, a clean and safe environment, health, quality of life. And Article 29 recognizes children's rights to education that develops personality, talents and potential, respecting human rights and the natural environment.

— *Dr. Alexandra Wandel*
World Future Council

The UN Sustainable Development Goals

At the United Nations Rio+20 Conference on Sustainable Development in 2012, governments and people came together to find pathways for a safer, more fair, and greener world for all. Everyone agreed to take new action to end poverty, stop environmental problems, and build bridges to a more just future. In 283 paragraphs of *The Future We Want* Declaration, countries committed to defend human rights, steward resources, fight climate change and pollution, protect animals, plants and biodiversity, and look after oceans, mountains, wetlands and other special places.

In the United Nations, countries are committing to 17 new Sustainable Development Goals for the whole world, with targets for real actions on the ground. Clubs, governments, firms, schools and children have started over a thousand partnerships, and mobilized billions, to deliver. The future we want exists in the hearts and minds of our generation, and in the hands of us all.

— *Vuyelwa Kuuya*
Centre for International Sustainable Development Law (CISDL)

Voices of Future Generations Children's Book Series

United Nations
Educational, Scientific and
Cultural Organization

Under the patronage of
UNESCO

Thanks and Inspiring Resources

'Voices of Future Generations' International Commission
Warmest thanks to the International Commission, launched in 2014 by His Excellency Judge CG Weeramantry, UNESCO Peace Education Research Award Laureate, which supports, guides and profiles this new series of Children's Books Series, including Ms Alexandra Wandel (WFC), Dr Marie-Claire Cordonier Segger (CISDL), Dr Kristiann Allen (New Zealand), Ms Irina Bokova (UNESCO), Mr Karl Hansen (Trust for Sustainable Living), Ms Emma Hopkin (UK), Dr Ying-Shih Hsieh (EQPF), Dr Maria Leichner-Reynal (Uruguay), Ms Melinda Manuel (PNG), Ms Julia Marton-Lefevre (IUCN), Dr James Moody (Australia), Ms Anna Oposa (The Philippines), Professor Kirsten Sandberg (UN CRC Chair), Ms Patricia Chaves (UN DSD), Dr Marcel Szabo (Hungary), Dr Christina Voigt (Norway), Ms Gabrielle Sacconaghi-Bacon (Moore Foundation), Ms Marcela Orvañanos de Rovzar (UNICEF Mexico) and others.

The World Future Council consists of 50 eminent global changemakers from across the globe. Together, they work to pass on a healthy planet and just societies to our children and grandchildren. (www.worldfuturecouncil.org)

United Nations Education, Science and Culture Organization (UNESCO) which celebrates its 70th Anniversary throughout 2015, strives to build networks among nations that enable humanity's moral and intellectual solidarity by mobilizing for education, building intercultural understanding, pursuing scientific cooperation, and protecting freedom of expression. (en.unesco.org)

The **United Nations Committee on the Rights of the Child (CRC)** is the body of 18 independent experts that monitors implementation of the Convention on the Rights of the Child, and its three Optional Protocols, by its State parties. (www.ohchr.org)

United Nations Environment Programme (UNEP) provides leadership and encourages partnership in caring for the environment by inspiring, informing, and enabling nations and peoples to improve their quality of life without compromising that of future generations. (www.unep.org)

International Union for the Conservation of Nature (IUCN) envisions a just world that values and conserves nature, working to conserve the integrity and diversity of nature and to ensure that any use of natural resources is equitable and ecologically sustainable. (www.iucn.org)

Centre for International Sustainable Development Law (CISDL) supports understanding, development and implementation of law for sustainable development by leading legal research through scholarship and dialogue, and facilitating legal education through teaching and capacity-building. (www.cisdl.org)

Trust for Sustainable Living and its Living Rainforest Centre exist to further the understanding of sustainable living in the United Kingdom and abroad through high-quality education. (www.livingrainforest.org)

Environmental Quality Protection Foundation (EQPF) established in 1984 is the premier ENGO in Taiwan. Implementing environmental education, tree plantation, and international participation through coordinating transdisciplinarity resources to push forward environmental and sustainable development in our time.

Under the patronage of
UNESCO

United Nations
Educational, Scientific and
Cultural Organization

About the 'Voices of Future Generations' Series

To celebrate the 25th Anniversary of the United Nations Convention on the Rights of the Child, the Voices of Future Generations Children's Book Series, led by the United Nations and a consortium of educational charities including the World Future Council (WFC), the Centre for International Sustainable Development Law (CISDL), the Environmental Quality Protection Foundation (EQPF), the Fundacion Ecos and the Trust for Sustainable Living (TSL) among others, also the Future Generations Commissioners of several countries, and international leaders from the UN Division for Sustainable Development, the UN Committee on the Rights of the Child, the UN Education, Science and Culture Organisation (UNESCO), the International Union for the Conservation of Nature (IUCN), and other international organizations, has launched the new Voices of Future Generations Series of Children's Books.

Every year we feature stories from our selected group of child authors, inspired by the outcomes of the Earth Summit, the Rio+20 United Nations Conference on Sustainable Development (UNCSD) and the world's Sustainable Development Goals, and by the Convention on the Rights of the Child (CRC) itself. Our junior authors, ages 8-12, are concerned about future justice, poverty, the global environment, education and children's rights. Accompanied by illustrations, each book profiles creative, interesting and adventurous ideas for creating a just and greener future, in the context of children's interests and lives.

We aim to publish the books internationally in ten languages, raising the voices of future generations and spread their messages for a fair and sustainable tomorrow among their peers and adults, worldwide. We welcome you to join us in support of this inspiring partnership, at www.vofg.org.